Bomb scare

Tessa Krailing

Nelson

Rocky was watching the television.
His Mum came in.
'What are you watching?' she asked.
'It's the News,' said Rocky.
'It's about this bomb scare.
Someone found a bomb in a park and
called the police.'
'You shouldn't be inside watching television
on a lovely day like this,' said Mum.
'Go and play outside.'

Rocky met Kevin in the Square.
'Let's play football,' he said.
'Can't stop, I'm in a hurry,' Kevin said.
'I'm going to buy something.'

Next Rocky met Ben.
'Let's play football,' he said.
But Ben didn't want to.
'It's too hot,' he said.
'Let's just sit down over there.'
They went over to a bench.
'Look at that box,' said Ben.

Rocky and Ben looked at the box.
There were a lot of wires sticking out.
'I know what it is,' Rocky said.
'It's a bomb!'

6

'I was watching the News just before
I came out.
It was all about a bomb scare.
Someone left a bomb in a park.'
'What shall we do?' asked Ben.
'There's Fred,' said Rocky.
'Let's tell him about it.'

The boys went over to Fred.
'Come and look at this,' said Rocky.
'There's a box with wires sticking out.
We think it's a bomb,' said Ben.
Fred looked at the box.
'Is it ticking?' he asked.
They listened. The box wasn't ticking.
'No,' said Ben. 'There's no sound coming from it.'
'Then it's not a bomb,' said Fred.

Fred went away.
'I'm sure it's a bomb,' said Rocky.
'We'd better call the police.
That's what they did on television.'

Rocky called the police.
'Hello, is that the police?' he asked.
'We've found a bomb.
It's in the park in Wellington Square.
It's in a box with wires sticking out.'

The police came very quickly.
'Now where is this bomb?' asked PC Kent.
'Over there on the bench,' said Ben.

Some people came to see what was going on.
WPC Clark kept them away from the bomb.
'You must keep back,' she said.
'It may go off and hurt someone.'
'We will get a man who knows all about bombs.
He will make it safe,' said PC Kent.

The man came very quickly.
He looked at the box and the wires.
'What will he do?' Rocky asked.
'How will he make it safe?'

'I don't know,' Ben said.
'But we will be famous.
We've saved Wellington Square from a bomb.
We will be on television.'

'This may not be a bomb,' the man said.
'But we'd better be sure.
The box must be made safe.
I will blow it up.'

WPC Clark made the people stand back.
'Stay over there,' she said.
'The box is going to be blown up.'

Just then Kevin came back into the park.
'What's going on?' he asked Rocky.
'See that box with the wires sticking out?
It's a bomb,' said Rocky.
'That man knows all about bombs.
He is going to blow it up.'
'That's not a bomb!' Kevin shouted.
'That's my radio!'

19

'That's my radio,' Kevin called.
'I was mending it!
I went to buy some wire.
Please don't blow up my radio!'

But no-one listened to Kevin.
PC Kent kept him away from the box and
soon it was all over.
There was a bright flash.
There was a loud bang.
The man had blown up the radio!

The bright flash and loud bang made
the people frightened.
'It's all over,' PC Kent said.
'The bomb has been made safe.'
'But it wasn't a bomb!' Kevin shouted.
'Who said it was a bomb?
Who called the police and said my radio
was a bomb?'

'Let's go,' Rocky said.
'Let's go before he finds out who said
it was a bomb!'
'He shouldn't have left it there,' said Ben.
'We won't be famous now!' said Rocky.

Fred wasn't very pleased.
'What a mess,' he said.
'What a mess they made in my park!'
Kevin wasn't very pleased.
'What a mess they made of my radio,' he said.